ROGER EVANS
PLAYING KEYBOARDS

Scottish & Irish Songs

First Published 1991
© International Music Publications

Exclusive Distributors
International Music Publications
Southend Road, Woodford Green,
Essex IG8 8HN, England

215-2-684

Introduction

This entertaining collection of Irish and Scottish songs has been specially chosen and arranged to be easy and enjoyable to play.

This music is perfect for everyone who learned to play with the *Playing Keyboards* book and cassette. It is also ideal for everyone who wants to play good music easily on modern keyboards.

Simply follow these helpful hints and you can quickly start enjoying the music:

Playing Hints

The music in this book follows the same easy style used in the *Playing Keyboards* books:

Suggested Voices and Rhythms are given at the beginning of every tune, like this:

> Organ/Flute
> Ballad/Pops or Rock (Medium)

You can choose whichever settings suit your keyboard. Here, you chould choose either the Organ or Flute voice, and set a Ballad, Pops or Rock rhythm. If your keyboard does not have any of the suggested voices or rhythms, choose voices and rhythms which suit the music you are playing.

The suggested 'tempo' (speed) of the music is shown in brackets: (Medium). If your keyboard uses numbers to show the tempo of the music, you can follow this guide:

For Medium tempo, set the tempo control to between 90 and 120.
For Medium-Slow, set the tempo to 70 or 80.
For Slow, set the tempo to 60 or less.
For Medium-Fast, set the tempo to 130 to 150.

Adjust the tempo control of your keyboard to the suggested setting before you begin each tune. If you like, set the tempo a little slower than suggested until you are comfortable playing a new tune. If the suggested tempo doesn't seem right for a tune, change it to suit your own tastes.

Special Effects which you can add to the music are shown in brackets over some tunes:

(Arpeggio/Variation) — means you can add an automatic 'Arpeggio' to the backing of a tune if your keyboard has this effect; or you can use an auto chord accompaniment 'variation' which gives a 'rippling' effect.

Fingering — Finger numbers are shown in front of notes where the fingering is not obvious, and where the fingers need to move to different keys:

1 = thumb   2 = index finger   3 = middle finger   4 = ring finger   5 = little finger

Chords — You can play all of the music in this book with easy 'One Finger Chords', 'Casio Chords' or 'Single Finger Chords' — or you can use 'Fingered Chords'.

Chord symbols are shown over the music wherever a chord change is needed. Chords shown in brackets are optional, and may be left out for easy playing:

C(7) — means you can play a C7 chord, or a C chord.

(C7) — means this chord is not essential and may be left out if necessary.

All of the tunes are easier to play if the optional chords are left out. However, you will find the music usually sounds far better if *all* chords are played, so try and play them all if you can.

'Transposing' — Many keyboards have a very useful facility called a 'Transposer' which changes the pitch of the instrument. This is very helpful for music which is too high or too low for singing, and the 'Transposer' can also be used when you play along with certain other musical instruments, and for special effects.

For singing — If the music is too high for the singer, try setting the Transposer to B♭ (♭2 or −2). If the music is still too high, try setting it to G (♭5 or −5).

If the music is too low for the singer, try setting the Transposer to E♭ (♯3 or +3) or F (♯5 or +5).

Playing With Other Instruments — If you have friends who play B♭ instruments like the clarinet, trumpet or tenor saxophone, and you would like them to play along with you, *and read your music*, set the Transposer to B♭ (♭2 or −2). For E♭ instruments set the Transposer to E♭ (♯3 or +3).

(There is no need to use the Transposer when you play along with a guitar, flute, violin, recorder or most other instruments — as long as they 'tune' to your keyboard.)

You can also use the Transposer to give music a 'lift'. Try playing a tune through once. Then, without stopping, set the Transposer to C♯ (♯1 or +1), D (♯2 or +2) or higher — and play the tune again. (As with all special effects, it is best not to over-use this trick!)

Always remember to re-set the Transposer to C (0) when you have finished.

You can find more playing hints, easy-to-follow instruction and more good tunes in the *Playing Keyboards* book and songbooks, which are obtainable from your music dealer.

Wishing you many happy hours playing the music in this book.

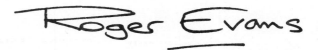

Galway Bay

Words and Music by DR. ARTHUR COLAHAN

Accordian or Violin/Strings
Ballad/Pops (Medium-Slow)

If you ev-er go a-cross the sea to Ire-land, Then may-be at the clos-ing of your day, You will sit and watch the moon rise o-ver Clad-dagh, And see the sun go down on Gal-way Bay. Just to hear a-gain the rip-ple of the trout stream, The wo-men in the mea-dows mak-ing hay, And to sit be-side a turf fire in the ca-bin, And

1. watch the bare-foot gos-soons at their play. If you

2. play.

Published by permission of PIGOTT & CO. LTD., Dublin.

How Can You Buy Killarney

Words and Music by HAMILTON KENNEDY,
FREDDIE GRUNDLAND, GERALD MORRISON & TED STEELS

Violin/Strings or Organ
Waltz (Medium)

I'll Take You Home Again, Kathleen

Adapted and Arranged by ROGER EVANS

Organ or Trumpet/Brass
Ballad/Pops (Slow) (Add Arpeggio/Variation)

It's A Great Day For The Irish

Words and Music by RODGER EDENS

Trombone or Trumpet/Brass
Swing (Medium-Fast)

The Kerry Dance

Adapted and Arranged by ROGER EVANS

Accordian, Organ or Flute
Slow Rock or 6-beat (Medium)
(Play Medium-Slow until you know the tune)

A Little Bit of Heaven

Words by J KEIRN BRENNAN
Music by ERNEST R BALL

Violin/Strings or Trumpet/Brass
Ballad/Pops (Medium-Slow)

Sure a lit-tle bit of Hea-ven fell from out the sky one day, And nest-led on the o-cean in a spot so far a-way; And when the an-gels found it, Sure it looked so sweet and fair, They said sup-pose we leave it, for it looks so peace-ful there. So, they sprink-led it with star-dust just to make the sham-rocks grow; 'Tis the on-ly place you'll find them no mat-ter where you go; Then they dot-ted it with sil-ver, To make its lakes so grand, And when they had it fin-ished sure they called it Ire-land.

That's An Irish Lullaby

Words and Music by J. R. SHANNON

Trumpet/Brass or Organ
Ballad/Pops (Medium)

O Danny Boy

Adapted and Arranged by ROGER EVANS

Organ or Flute
Ballad/Pops (Medium-Slow) (Add Variation/Arpeggio)

The Rose Of Tralee

Adapted and Arranged by ROGER EVANS

Flute/Clarinet or Organ
Waltz (Medium-Slow) (Add Variation/Arpeggio)

For short version, finish here.

When Irish Eyes Are Smiling

Words by CHAUNCEY OLCOTT and GEO GRAFF Jr
Music by ERNEST R BALL

Organ or Flute
Waltz (Medium-Slow)

Auld Lang Syne

Adapted and Arranged by ROGER EVANS

Violin/Strings or Bagpipes
Ballad/Pops (Medium-Slow) (Add Variation/Arpeggio)

A Good New Year

Adapted and Arranged by ROGER EVANS

Violin/Strings or Organ
Ballad/Pops (Medium)

Down In The Glen

Words and Music by HARRY GORDON and TOMMIE CONNOR

Trumpet/Brass
Waltz (Medium-Slow) (Add Variation/Arpeggio)

Lyrics under the staves:

At hush of ev - en - tide O'er the

hills be - yond the Clyde I go roam - ing to my

hea - ven Down in the glen. Though

hum - ble it may be, There an an - gel waits for

me In that love - ly, lit - tle hea - ven,

Down in the glen. A - cross the moon - lit

hea - ther my las - sie calls as I roam, 'Tis

The End Of The Road

Words and Music by WILLIAM DILLON and HARRY LAUDER

Organ
March or Ballad/Pops (Medium)

I Belong To Glasgow

Words and Music by WILL FYFFE

Accordion or Violin/Strings
Waltz (Medium)

I be - long to Glas - gow, dear old Glas - gow town. But what's the mat - ter with Glas - gow? For it's go - ing round and round. I'm on - ly a com - mon old work - ing chap, As a - ny - one can see, But when I get a cou - ple of drinks on a Sa - tur - day, Glas - gow be -

1. longs to me.

2. me.

My Love Is Like A Red, Red Rose

Adapted and Arranged by ROGER EVANS

Organ or Flute
Ballad/Pops (Medium or Medium-Fast)

For short version finish here. Alternatively, change to a different voice to play second time through.

Roamin' In The Gloamin'

Words and Music by HARRY LAUDER

Flute/Clarinet or Organ
Rock (Medium) or Ballad/Pops (Medium-Fast)

Instrumental

Roam - in' in the gloam - in' on the bon - nie banks of Clyde. Roam - in' in the gloam - in' wi' my las - sie by my side, When the sun has gone to rest, That's the time that we love best. O, it's love - ly roam - in' in the

1. gloam - in'.

2. - in'.

Scotland The Brave

Adapted and Arranged by ROGER EVANS

L.H. C D E F G
. 5 4 3 2 1

Organ or Bagpipe
March or Pops (Medium-Fast)

For short version, finish here.

Skye Boat Song

Adapted and Arranged by ROGER EVANS

Flute/Clarinet or Accordion
Waltz (Medium-Slow) (Add Arpeggio/Variation)

10/91

31